THE MAGIC OF COLOR

BY THOMAS H. WOLF

ILLUSTRATED BY NED SEIDLER

THE ODYSSEY PRESS · NEW YORK

A search for colors as old as civilization led Mediterranean scribes and artists to the ink sac of the cuttlefish, FAR LEFT, *which supplied them with sepia. From the tiny scale insect called cochineal,* BOTTOM LEFT, *early Peruvians and Mexicans obtained a deep carmine red later much valued in Renaissance Europe. Azurite (blue) and malachite (green) are often found together, both of them being crystals of copper carbonate; for use as pigments they were powdered and mixed with a vehicle such as animal fat. The leaves of the indigo plant were used in dyeing textiles, producing a dark blue; the more highly prized "imperial" purple was obtained from the murex shell (the production center being Tyre, on the Phoenician coast). The mineral cinnabar,* ABOVE, *today a source of mercury, was long used to make orangey reds. Charred bone and horn produced bone black.*

ACKNOWLEDGMENTS: *The Bergman Associates: 38R, 39T. The Cooper Union Museum: 12. Zvonko Glyck:* cover, *43. Kroeller-Mueller Museum, Otterlo, Holland: detail from* A Road with Cypresses and Stars *by Vincent Van Gogh, 6; detail from* Breakfast *by Paul Signac, 32, photos by Francis G. Mayer. Kunsthistorisches Museum, Vienna: detail from* Hunters in the Snow *by Pieter Brueghel, 34. National Gallery of Art, Washington, D.C.* *Chester Dale Collection: detail from* Self Portrait, 1889, *by Paul Gauguin, 40. Phillips Collection, Washington, D.C.:* Egyptian Curtain *by Henri Matisse, 33. Emil Schulthess, Conzett & Huber: 9.* The Tests for Color Blindness *by S. Ishihara, copyright Kanehara Shuppan Co., Ltd., Tokyo: 37. Wadsworth Atheneum, Hartford: detail from* Beach at Trouville *by Claude Monet, 35. Western Electric: 36. Carl Zeiss, Oberkochen, 38T 38L.*

The purest and most thoughtful minds are those
which love color the most. — JOHN RUSKIN: The Stones of Venice

A BLACK CAT is bad luck. Envy is green. Passion is purple. A coward is yellow. If you're blue, that's bad. But if you are true blue, that's good. We damn blue laws. We cheer blue ribbons. And we hope that our futures will consist exclusively of red letter days, but red is precisely the wrong color for our financial accounts. In a thousand of our idioms we unconsciously reveal the first and most important meaning of color to man: as a talisman beckoning friendly gods and warding off evil spirits. ■ Primitive man, seeing about him the hues of nature but unable

Our whole world of color ultimately comes from the sun.
In his inspired assault on the canvas, Vincent van Gogh was
returning to the sun all the colors the sun had given him.

to duplicate them or to account for them, assigned magical properties to color. ■ One million years ago, our ancestors, noting that blood is red and believing that the color itself contained a life-giving ingredient, daubed their dead with red clay to ensure them eternal life. This was probably man's first use of color. Later, the early Greeks believed that all matter was composed of four elements, to each of which they assigned a color. Earth was green; air, yellow; water, blue; fire, red. ■ Long before scientists knew that the sun was the source of all color, the Egyptians bestowed on Ra, their sun god, the rank of first king of Egypt. And because purple was the most difficult of all col-

7

Emerging rays fan out, red bending least.

Throughout the history of mankind, colors were thought to be part of the objects around us. In January 1666 this view was exploded by a 23-year-old investigator, Isaac Newton. "Having darkened my chamber," he later wrote, "and made a small hole in my window shuts to let in a convenient quantity of the Sun's light, I placed my Prisme at his entrance, that it might be there refracted to the opposite wall." This arrangement (with later refinements giving the full visible spectrum, ABOVE), made it clear to Newton that colors are not "qualifications" of light but are already contained in sunlight itself. (He even regathered his colors and produced white from them.) We can see the colors contained in sunlight whenever we catch sight of a rainbow. Rainbows are formed in fine rain droplets, but also in any other fine spray—as in mist over Victoria Falls in Africa, RIGHT. A ray of sunlight is first bent as it enters each water droplet, is reflected once on the inner periphery of the droplet, then is bent and dispersed again as it emerges into air. To produce fainter, outside rainbow, light is bounced twice within droplet, and colors are reversed.

ors for the Egyptians to duplicate, purple became the prerogative of Ra and of all kings since. ■ Throughout history, gems have been treasured less for their decorative beauty than for the potency of their color. Turquoise, the ancients believed, could detect poison; amethyst, ensure sobriety; ruby, preserve health. But different human societies endowed the same colors with different powers. To signify her purity, a Western bride wears white, an Indian bride wears red, and an Israeli bride, yellow. ■ Not only do societies attach different significance to certain colors, but different individuals are differently aware of them. Because blue and green are the most common of nature's colors, they are the ones we are least conscious of. Indeed in certain primitive cultures no word exists for them. Blue is "like the sky" and green, "like the leaves." ■ In our modern society, the average person can call to mind only about thirty names of colors (excluding shades and tones). And even these names have undergone vast changes. (Try asking a sales girl for nankeen mittens or gules socks—but in medieval England she'd have given you

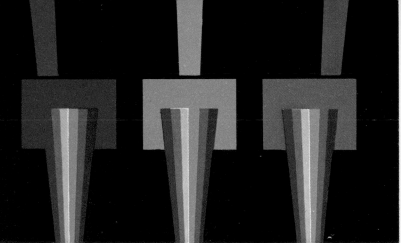

A filter absorbs all the colors of the spectrum except its own color, which passes through. In effect, the colors held back are subtracted from the original combination. Colors in nature (TOP RIGHT) are also "subtractive": leaf absorbs (subtracts) all colors but green, apple absorbs all colors but red. In green light (MIDDLE), apple finds no red to reflect back, hence looks dark. In red light (BOTTOM), it is the leaf that looks dark—for lack of green rays to throw back.

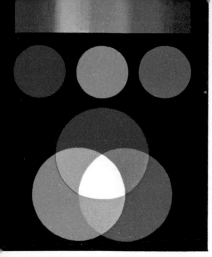

Balanced sets of red, green, and blue make up the primaries of light. Such "additive primaries" can be selected from the spectrum so that three beams will blend to produce white. Wherever two beams overlap, intermediate hues appear.

yellow gloves and red hose without an instant's hesitation.) ■ If color played a dominant role in the lives of our superstitious ancestors, it plays a hardly less important part in our super-scientific society. Color, for example, is at the heart of the quantum theory of physics, which is basic to today's atomic science. Scientifically speaking, color is the visible portion of the electromagnetic spectrum of radiant energy—a spectrum that runs all the way from long radio waves to X-rays and gamma rays. Just as our ears can hear only a very limited range of sound frequencies, so our eyes can see only a minuscule portion of the spectrum. Certain butterflies are able to see ultraviolet colors, although such hues remain invisible to humans. It was as recently as 1666 that Isaac Newton, noticing how sunlight was affected by passing through a glass prism, formulated his theory that white light is really made up of all the colors in the spectrum. ■ It is ironic, considering all man's superstitions, thoughts, and theories about color, that color apparently is not a necessary condition of man's existence on this planet. Evidently, we would be perfectly able to live, adapt, and prosper in a black-

11

and-white world, drab as it might be. The explanation for this is that man's visual recognition of objects, an ability that is basic to his survival, depends on shape, not color. If this seems strange, one should remember that many animals on this earth, like dogs, lack the nerve cells to perceive color at all. ■ Early man found his colors in nature—in plants and berries, in roots and leaves, in clays and minerals, and in the bones and vital fluids of the insects, birds, fish, and other animals with whom he shared his patch of earth. Almost everything in nature was capable of providing man with color once he knew how to extract it. ■ The ink sack of the cuttle-fish, native to European and Asian waters, is the source of a brown pigment called *sepia*. ■ From the gland of the murex snail, found in the Mediterranean, the Phoenicians pro-duced the famous Tyrian purple dye, a rare color of great

Early interest in color appears in this intricately woven mitt of the third century B.C. Found at Ch'ang-Sha in southeastern China, its brown and honey-colored silk has been woven into small geometric figures set in a larger trellis of lozenges, picked up at intervals with a silk thread dyed vermilion through the use of powdered cinnabar. (FRONT END PAPER *shows original cinnabar ore.*)

value because thousands of snails were required to produce minute amounts of dye. ■ The indigo plant produced a dark blue dye when its leaves were fermented and the resulting solution oxidized. ■ The great Roman encyclopedist Pliny the Elder, in his *Natural History*, describes not only what colors can be obtained from certain plants and animals, but in great detail gives instructions on how to make such dyes as indigo and murex. Artists in the past ground the crystals of scores of minerals to produce desired colors. Cinnabar—a mercury sulfide—was ground into powder that became the base for vermilion. Lapis lazuli was pounded to dust to produce the blue known by the min-

By a tradition dating from pre-Columbian times, Mexicans have long cultivated a variety of Opuntia *cactus that attracts the parasitic cochineal insect, which yields a dye of a vivid carmine red. Though cochineal dyes have lost ground to their synthetic counterparts, they are still used to color foods.*

eral's name. Azurite and malachite, both copper carbonates, gave early man other blues and greens. ■ By charring teeth, ivory, and bones, our ancestors obtained black pigments. ■ Because different flora and fauna are indigenous to different parts of the world, the colors used by various peoples were often a practical matter of regional availability rather than one of aesthetic preference. It was easy enough for a Mexican to harvest cochineal bugs for his reds. But this color was out of the European's reach until the Spanish conquistadores conquered the New World. Although gold and spices of the East were powerful motives behind the early voyages of discovery —and the subsequent wars over trade routes—new and exotic colors were also high on the merchants' priority lists. ■ Man's earliest use of color was to decorate his body—a practice that continues today to the tune of a multi-million-dollar yearly cosmetics bill in the United States alone. Since the purpose

Chinese actor's face. Color symbolism is an important communicative feature in all theater (hero in white, villain in black). The Chinese developed hua-lien *("painted face") to a remarkable degree, revealing character through the standardization of both design and color of makeup.*

14

Hex design, ABOVE, is from barn in Pennsylvania Dutch country. Such designs, often with echoes of patterns of stained glass and inlaid floors of Medieval Europe, were originally talismans, to frighten off witches. Red, the color of life (blood), is used in many cultures to ward off death. Sand paintings are made for related but broader purposes by Indians of the Southwest, whose colors (corn pollen, crushed minerals), are applied with the right hand and erased by sundown. Color and design determine which gods are invoked.

of this decoration was not beauty but talismanic protection against evil, it is not surprising that the symbolism of color has always played a major role in the religious life of the world. ■ In Christianity, white indicate purity and joy; red, charity; blue, truth; gree hope and life everlasting; purple, sorrow a suffering; black, death. And the English guage abounds with idioms reflecting this symbolism. To cite one example: "true comes from the costume of a Scottisl which, revolting against the dishonesty

Heraldry in its original function is seen in the figur English knight of A.D. 1300 displaying his arms on surcoat, and banner. (The three lions "passant gu represent England.) Later developments are the orna aissance shield with its helm, crest, and mantling personal arms of poet Geoffrey Chaucer, who beca titled to them after several years in the king's service.

royal family, chose the color signifying truth.
■ One of the earliest formal uses for color was in *heraldry*, a medieval system for identifying men in armor. There are seven heraldic colors: ~ (gold); *argent* (silver); *gules* (red); *azure* ~lue); *sable* (black); *vert* (green); *purpure* ~rple). Each signifies a specific virtue. At ~, each nobleman chose his own symbols ~colors, which he wore into battle or in ~ament to identify himself—otherwise, en~ clad in armor with his face hidden by ~r, he was unknown to friend or foe. He ~ wore a knit design over his armor (hence, ~*f arms*) or had his design painted on his ~. But eventually, it became the king's ~gative to assign armorial bearings and ~ to reward valorous deeds with especially ~d symbols and colors—like red, which at~ ~l to its bearer's courage. ■ The symbolism ~eraldic color was rigorously defined. So

Instant response to color is key to visual communication under stress. First line of numeral pennants reads 0, 2, 4, second line, 5, 7, 9. Square alphabet flags read C, L, O, Z. Red Cross uses Swiss flag with colors reversed; Arabs and Iranians substitute their own symbols.

17

were the combinations in which the colors might be used. One color could not be mixed, or abased, with another, or the virtues represented by the colors would be diluted; nor could silver and gold be placed one on top of the other. ■ The notion of a *stain on one's escutcheon* derives from the theory that a bad knight would be punished by incorporating one of two abased (mixed) tints, *murrey* (purple red) or *tenné* (orange), into his coat of arms. Since, however, a knight would have been unlikely to bear a coat of arms advertising his iniquities, stains were probably never actually used. Another heraldic tradition of color, one that has carried over to modern times, is that of huntsmen wearing "pink" (the shade is actually scarlet). The reason for this color is not for easy recognition in the field but because in the days when

Color of bird feathers is produced in two ways: In one system, feathers hold little grains of pigment—usually melanin, giving a wide range of browns, and lipochrome, for red and yellow. (Assorted pigment grains, in pairs, produce mixed colors.) In the other system, a top layer of colorless cells produces greens and blues by prism effects, though underlying pigments are still browns and yellows. Peacock colors show both mechanisms.

19

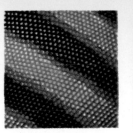

*Surprising, misleading, concealing, reminding, the resourcefulness of the living world is most dazzling in its manipulation of color. The poisonous fly agaric (Amanita muscaria) carries its beauty as a warning of its deadliness; vivid color bands pass over the hundreds of minute lenses of a fly's eye (not being pigments, they fade at the insect's death); the scales of our Southern corn snake render it close to invisible if it holds still; the iridescent colors of a Madagascar beetle arise from numerous thin, partially transparent layers that break up the light. Innocent-looking pansy (*ON FACING PAGE*) is— like all flowers—engaged in attracting insects to help promote exchange of genetic material between the sexes; in the darkness of its inside cavity, the abalone secretes layer upon layer of iridescent mother-of-pearl; the Owl Butterfly, which has a run-of-the-mill topside, can startle predators with its "eyes" by suddenly unfolding the underside of its hindwings; the Gila monster advertises its venomousness through the distinctive coloring of its beady scales.*

the king owned all hunting lands, those he allowed to hunt wore the king's scarlet livery. Man sees color everywhere in nature. But nature is a fickle artist, and her colors are constantly changing. Sometimes these changes are real—in autumn, for instance, when a chemical change takes place within the leaves. But often these changes in color are merely apparent, as in the brilliantly hued fish that turns a drab monochrome out of water. ■ To understand color in nature, we must understand something about the various ways in which beams of light reach the human eye and how the eye reacts to them. Nobody knows exactly how the human eye functions, but it is thought that the retina is physically composed of two different kinds of light-perceiving nerves: rods and cones. It is the cones, apparently, that are able to perceive color. Different sets of cones are stimulated by different wave lengths of light —that is, colors. The cones react to the primary colors of light: red, green, and blue. And just as all colors can be achieved from these three, so the brain mixes them in appropriate propor-

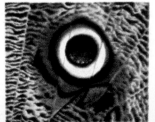
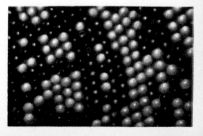

tion for us to "see" natural colors. The simplest explanation of color is that natural pigments in plants and animals absorb certain colors and reflect back to our eyes only the remaining limited portion of the spectrum, which we see as specific colors. ■ But before the light reaches our eyes from objects in nature, it may be distorted in a variety of ways. There are two common tricks of nature which affect color. One is called *interference.* It is caused not by pigmentation but by a transparent film, like oil on a fish's body. When light strikes this film, some of it is reflected from the mirror-like surface of the film, while some of it passes through

The woodcock's protective coloration begins with its general coloring, which matches that of the forest leaves. But it also includes countershading: the bird's naturally illuminated side—its back—carries darker pigmentation than its shaded underside, making its presence difficult to detect.

the film and is reflected by the opaque background beneath the film—the scales on the fish's body. Under certain circumstances, this double reflection from the top and bottom of the transparent film interferes with colors of one or another wave length, and they are not seen. Different wave lengths of light are affected by the varying thickness of the transparent film. This is why an oil slick, constantly changing in thickness, seems to change color. ■ The second of nature's color tricks is known as *refraction,* which occurs when an object like a drop of water, acting as a tiny prism, breaks up light into its spectral colors, as in the case of a rainbow. It was this phenomenon that Newton witnessed when sunlight passed through his prism. ■ Color, as a means of camouflage, is of vital importance in the animal world. Even the "loudest" and, to human eyes, most distinctive animal markings appear to serve the

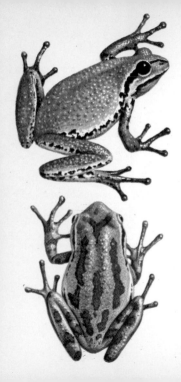

purpose of camouflage. The wildly striped zebra or tiger may become almost invisible against certain backgrounds. In many species of birds, the male, whose role is to forage for food among the dappled leaves of the forest and the multicolored flowers of the field, is endowed with vivid markings which nevertheless blend into his matted surroundings, while his mate is protected in her sedentary role of nest-sitter by a far duller plumage which matches the dried-out grasses from which the nest is built. Probably the most elaborate example of color and camouflage among all living creatures is found in the flatid bug, a moth that lives in colonies. Some members of the colony are red, some white, some green, and some multicolored. Whenever they alight, they arrange themselves on a branch in such a way that their pattern, seen from even a close distance, resembles a flower growing on the branch—a flower, oddly enough, that does not even

The Pacific tree frog, Hyla regilla—champion aerialist, broad jumper, and swimmer—depends on quick color changes for its survival. Enlargement and contraction of the dark color cells (melanophores) in the frog's skin make possible radical changes in both color and pattern in less than ten minutes.

exist in nature. ■ Although hunters have always used it to advantage, camouflage by man has generally been restricted to warfare and has become a "science" only since World War I. It took the bloody battles of 1914 to teach the French Army that madder-red pants and blue tunics offered enemy riflemen too easy a target. However, color has become less important in military camouflage since recent technological advances in radar, infra-red photography, and even satellites are no longer deceived by what fools the human eye. ■ If man finds less use for color in military camouflage, he nevertheless finds new uses for it all the time. For example, many species and sub-species of birds can only be distinguished by examining minuscule variations in feather coloring with a spectrophotometer. Without this accurate system of identification, hundreds of bird species would remain unclassified. ■ Man's world of

Camouflage, pioneered by the Germans, was well established in all armies by World War II. Seen from above, this 1937 RAF "Fairey Battle" blends into landscape, disruptive patterns contributing to difficulty of recognition. Undersides of planes were often painted a dull black to thwart searchlights.

25

In pigment colors, balanced yellows, reds, and blues are the primaries.

Color wheel brings out relations between pigment colors. Outer ring contains three primary pigments (red, yellow, blue), with the complementary to each placed diametrically across from it—green across from red, violet across from yellow, orange across from blue. Center spot (black), shows results of mixing two such complementaries in equal proportions; inner circle shows results of mixing them unequally—more green than red gives dark green, more red than green, reddish brown.

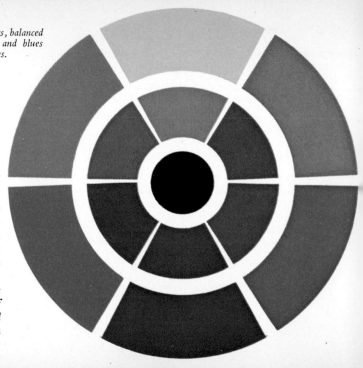

color underwent a major scientific revolution about a century ago. Its cause, like that of so many other scientific discoveries, was accidental. In 1858 an 18-year-old British medical student named William Henry Perkin was trying to make quinine synthetically. Instead, he ended up with a blue-red dye obtained by distilling a coal-tar. "Perkin's mauve," the first aniline dye, was put on the market commercially just one year later. Perkin had created the first synthetic color. From this point on, man was never again dependent on nature for his palette of colors. ■ Indeed, in recent years synthetic dyes have become so highly developed that thousands of new colors are made every year. ■ In order to make sense of

Triangle (CENTER) proposed by the German poet Goethe presents a wealth of interlocked harmonies. Goethe worked out his triangle in such a way that separate configurations within it lent themselves to psychological interpretation.

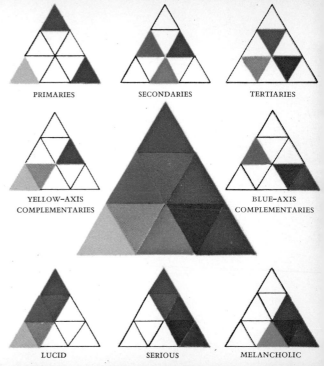

PRIMARIES SECONDARIES TERTIARIES

YELLOW–AXIS COMPLEMENTARIES BLUE–AXIS COMPLEMENTARIES

LUCID SERIOUS MELANCHOLIC

Any hue (for instance, red) can appear in our environment in modifications of saturation ("value," "intensity") as well as in modifications of lightness (on a scale from white to black)—and usually occurs in both modifications at the same time. In this experiment, a single hue (red), is shown as it is "pulled" in the direction of white, gray, and black.

their infinite number, several international classification systems have been devised to measure scientifically and to identify the hue, value, and chroma of all colors. Two of the best known systems are the Ostwald and the Munsell. ■ Each shade, tint, and tone seems different to our eyes when set in a different background. One of the first persons to study this phenomenon was the 19th-century French chemist Michel Chevreul, director of the famed Gobelins rug factory. Complaints about the quality of certain colors in Gobelin rugs led him to a life-long study of "the phenomena of the contrast of colors." His work on the effect of contiguous colors on one another greatly influenced the Impressionist painters' use of color. ■ They followed the theory that color as an exact quality had no existence; that a yellow vase was affected by its reflected surroundings. Even shadows were not the absence of color, but con-

A variety of tactics are available to help colors harmonize. Colors in top triangle clash; but pastel versions of these same colors harmonize easily—partly because white admixtures form a bond between them. Strong red and green (UPPER RIGHT) *fatigue eyes' color receptors in alternation, setting up vibration. Design itself is not at fault, however: in blue and yellow it looks perfectly stable.*

tained colors complementary to the object casting the shadow. They were stimulated by the idea that while the mind knew the foliage of a mountain to be green, as the mountain receded into the distance the atmosphere, acting as a filter, caused the eye to see it in shades of blue and lavender. Following the lead of Delacroix, to whom "gray was the enemy of all painting," they banished the earth colors from their palettes and used only the colors of the spectrum. These were not to be mixed with each other, but only with white. By laying the unmixed complementary constituent colors side by side in short, distinct brush strokes they allowed them to intensify one another. The object of their method is easily realized when we examine the color wheel (p. 26): brilliant colors tend

Stare at star in lower right corner of yellow field for half a minute, then switch gaze to single star. "Afterimage" flag will appear, formed of colors complementary to those above.

Barrett Browning when she wrote: *"Yes," I answered you last night;/ "No," this morning, sir, I say;/ Colors seen by candle light/ Will not look the same by day.* ■ Like so many other folklore notions, the idea that color affects people psychologically has been found to have a scientific basis. We speak of the red end of the spectrum's colors as warm; the violet end as cool. And it has recently been discovered that in fact the warm colors actually quicken the pulse and raise the blood pressure of the beholder, both of which effects would tend to make him feel warm; while cool colors reduce pulse rates and blood pressures. Blue, for example, has been reported by some observers to decrease glandular activity in humans, even to the point interfering with the healing of wounds, and to retard the development of certain plants. ■ The effect of color on human morale and efficiency has been widely studied to diminish in intensity or become grayer as they are mixed with each other. This application of vibrant broken colors compensated for the physical inability of pigments to duplicate light. The closer one comes to an Impressionist picture the less intelligible are the heavy layers of juxtaposed paints, but seen from a proper distance the effect of luminosity and unity is realized. It was Seurat and other *pointillistes* who first tried to formularize this optical mixture of colors on the scientific basis outlined by Chevreul. The *pointillistes* used dabs of color smaller and more uniform in size than those of the impressionists. ■ Since the Impressionists, man's concept of color has never been the same. What the Impressionists discovered bore out the observations of Elizabeth

'Cloisonnisme,' *or compartmentalization, is put to use in* ainting *done in his later years by Henri Matisse. It is used* a *composition as a whole and in Egyptian curtain,* RIGHT.

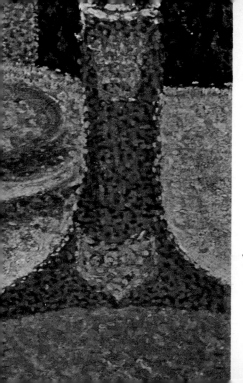

Seurat and Signac were concerned about the deadening effect of the direct use of pigments in painting—green paint to render a green bench, brown to render a brown one. By making up green from a swarm of blue and yellow dots, or brown from a swarm of red and green ones, they hoped to bring a new luminousness to the canvas. (The technique is called pointillisme.) Their success can be gauged from Signac's Breakfast.

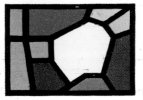

Used to full strength, colors normally clash when placed next to each other (TOP). Black partitions can prevent this. This technique, known as cloisonnisme, is also seen in medieval stained glass.

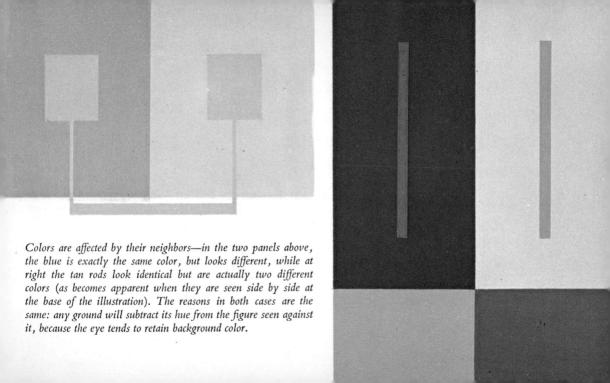

Colors are affected by their neighbors—in the two panels above, the blue is exactly the same color, but looks different, while at right the tan rods look identical but are actually two different colors (as becomes apparent when they are seen side by side at the base of the illustration). The reasons in both cases are the same: any ground will subtract its hue from the figure seen against it, because the eye tends to retain background color.

Although a mastery of the resources of color marks the work of all great painters, it is far from following the same channels in each. In painting his Hunters in the Snow, *the Fleming Pieter Brueghel set out to render the bleak chill of deep winter in his native country. Working in the brown regions of his palette (and even adding a touch of green to the blue of the sky to prevent it from giving warmth), he left us a telling account of what January meant in the snows of northern Europe. Impressionist Claude Monet, three centuries later, took a very different view of the artist's job. That the scene in front of him was a boardwalk at a fashionable resort meant little to him—what counted was the exact quality of the light reaching his eyes from each spot of light and shade. "When I see a canvas by Monet," said his fellow-painter Berthe Morisot, "I know exactly which way to slant my sunshade."*

for business as well as psychological reasons. When the Bureau of Internal Revenue recently repainted its card-punch subsection in bright pastels of high reflectivity, average productivity increased over 5 percent per employee. ■ Hospitals and manufacturers choose exactly opposite colors for their own purposes. The manufacturer wants his wares to attract the attention of potential customers so he chooses exciting colors for packages, often purposely using colors that clash. The hospital's neutral tones or gay pastels are selected for their ability to soothe and cheer. ■ Nowhere does color play a more important sales role than in the world of fashion. Consumer preferences appear to be cyclical, and a color that is "in" this year may be "out" next year but back in a decade. Actually colors

To distinguish similar items by color coding seems simple—but can become complicated. In this telephone switching unit, color technology is keeping pace with communications.

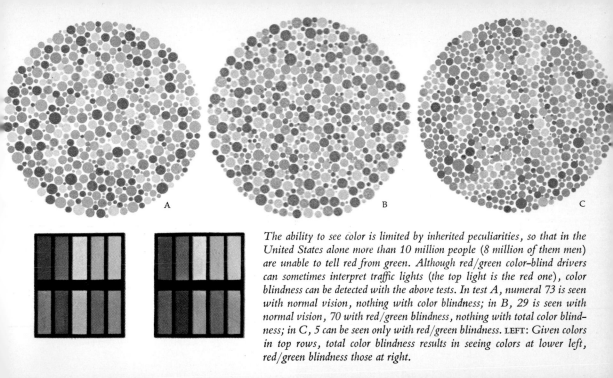

The ability to see color is limited by inherited peculiarities, so that in the United States alone more than 10 million people (8 million of them men) are unable to tell red from green. Although red/green color-blind drivers can sometimes interpret traffic lights (the top light is the red one), color blindness can be detected with the above tests. In test A, numeral 73 is seen with normal vision, nothing with color blindness; in B, 29 is seen with normal vision, 70 with red/green blindness, nothing with total color blindness; in C, 5 can be seen only with red/green blindness. LEFT: Given colors in top rows, total color blindness results in seeing colors at lower left, red/green blindness those at right.

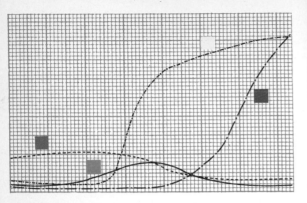

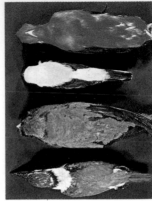

Miltown Crystals

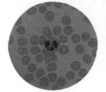

Blood Cells

Lupus attack

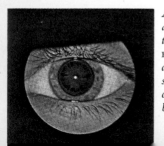

A sensitive analysis of bird colors is given by the spectrophotometer—a device that beams colors at specimens one hue at a time, recording the response on a photocell. This allows colors of (FROM TOP TO BOTTOM) the cock-of-the-rock, oriole, quetzal, and kingfisher to be described exactly (see curves). Birds are notorious for the way in which scores of varieties, differing in minute gradations of plumage color, confuse the borderlines between species. LEFT: *Eye is being examined by light internally reflected from within it, revealing a cataract.*

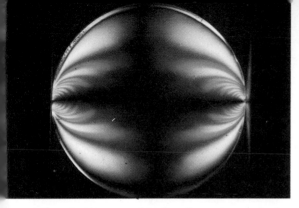

When plastic is squeezed in clamp (ABOVE), rays of polarized light travel through it at varying speeds. Their colors, as they recombine, show pattern of stress. This technique is now widely used in product design in industry.

The three photomicrographs (LEFT), from top to bottom, show the structure of meprobamate crystals as seen under polarized light, the structure of normal blood cells as brought out by staining, and blood cells invaded by lupus, also stained.

change less than nomenclature, and Madison Avenue devotes a great deal of time and money to inventing new and appealing descriptions, like autumn haze, misty morn, Spanish melon, and persimmon. ■ Colors as codes or signals play a major role in our lives; if you doubt it, try crossing a street when the light is red. Increasingly certain colors are being used to signify certain dangers: the purple propeller on a yellow field indicates atomic radiation; green designates the location of first aid equipment; and red, of course, signifies fire-fighting apparatus. ■ Almost no tool in the hands of the scientist is more versatile or more important than color. By bending, reflecting, refracting, diffracting, polarizing, and generally making the wave lengths of light behave in a controlled manner, the scientist is able to perform tests which would otherwise be denied him. For instance, scientists can measure the depth and density of a great variety of transparent materials by analyzing the colors reflected from them. ■ Color also permits chemists to analyze the composition of various substances. When minerals are heated to high temperatures, they emit characteristic color patterns. With the aid of a spectroscope, these colors can be measured and the mineral positively identified. ■ Much of our knowledge of the universe is the result of spectrographic examination of the stars. The so-called "red shift," for example, is the chief reason astronomers believe the universe is expanding. ■ In diffraction analysis, color is also used as an instrument of measurement. Diffraction describes the tendency of waves (of water, sound, or light) to spread out as they go around an obstacle. In so spreading, light waves take varying lengths of time to reach a given point and, as with interference, certain wave lengths cancel each other out. By analyzing the re-

Uninhibited colors of Gauguin's self-portrait set a challenge to modern techniques of color reproduction. The painting is first photographed on black-and-white film through green, red, and dark-blue filters (one at a time) and once again for black. The images on the four resulting films are then transferred to four printing plates in the form of minute dots etched into each plate. (A proof of each plate is shown ABOVE.) The angle of the lines of dots is different on each of the four plates—this ensures that each colored dot prints on white paper rather than on top of another dot (see enlargement, RIGHT). The four plates are then printed in the appropriate four inks, in the order shown in the strip at RIGHT. Fidelity to the original depends on a variety of factors—among them trueness of filters, control over dots, quality of inks, and hairbreadth accuracy in the way plates are positioned during printing. Today's achievements in color printing are a synthesis of the knowledge of color gained in the last three hundred years.

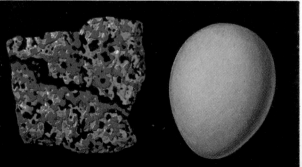

maining colors, scientists can learn much of value. ■ Light waves travel in one direction, but they vibrate in several. By the use of certain crystals, waves vibrating in all but one direction can be blocked out. This is known as *polarization*. With polarized light chemists can make many complicated analyses quickly and accurately. ■ "Colors" at the invisible ends of the spectrum also play important roles in science. Infra-red, at one end, not only eases stiff muscles, but has a multitude of scientific uses. ■ Ultraviolet, at the other end, is responsible for some of the most spectacular color displays known to man. When ultraviolet waves strike atoms of certain minerals, they precipitate electrical reactions which make the

Willemite (a zinc ore) and egg give off no noticeable light in daylight; but ultraviolet rays energize them so that in darkness egg has a pink glow and willemite emits green light from its manganese portions, red from its calcite.

previously colorless minerals emit light. This is known as *fluorescence.* ■ A related phenomenon is *phosphorescence,* in which a surface continues to glow after the radiation that has stimulated it has ceased. Phosphors are the secret that makes color television possible. The inside of the picture tube is coated with tiny dots of the primaries of light: red, green, and blue. When stimulated by appropriate electrical waves, these primaries are mixed to form all colors in the same way that the red, green, and blue cones in the human eye are stimulated to perceive all colors. ■ Ultraviolet light, sometimes called "black light" because it can't be seen, is the basis of much trick photography. If an object is painted with fluorescent paint, it will

At low pressure, neon gas in tube is readily excited to luminescence by electric discharge passing through it. The garish orange-red of these lamps can be changed to other colors by substitution of other gases—xenon gives blue.

A leading cause of red sunsets is the fact that when the sun is low on the horizon, it is seen through a long stretch of atmosphere—blue scatters out, red comes through.

be visible in ultraviolet light. But objects not so painted will be invisible. ■ Perhaps the most important use of that portion of the electromagnetic spectrum of radiant energy that is known as color is just now emerging from the laboratory. It is known as the *laser*. Wave lengths of certain colors are amplified and stimulated to produce a beam of light capable of performing tasks beyond the wildest dreams of only a decade ago. Using literally nothing but a beam of color, it will soon be possible to cut through steel or operate on a cancer deep in the brain. And in the world of communications, lasers open up channels for the future capable of carrying thousands of times the numbers of messages now possible with radio waves or telephone lines. Indeed, for all of its past, it looks as though the day of color is just beginning to dawn. It will be a colorful world tomorrow.

INDEX